MAGNETUDE

HOURS OF STICKY FUN

WITHOUT THE GOOEY MESS

BILL HADUCH
ILLUSTRATED BY CARYL BUHLER

PLANET DEXTER

Scholastic Inc.

New York Toronto London Auckland Sydney

Acknowledgments:
For Kenny Stevens, to whom I imagined I was writing.
Dedicated with love to Nita, Will, and Casey.

ISBN 0-590-96835-1

Text copyright © 1996 by Bill Haduch.
Illustrations copyright © 1996 by Caryl Buhler.
All rights reserved. Published by Scholastic Inc., 555 Broadway, New York, NY 10012, by arrangement with Addison-Wesley Publishing Company.

12 11 10 9 8 7 6 5 4   9/9 0 1/0

Printed in the U.S.A.   08

First Scholastic printing, October 1996

Cover design by C. Shane Sykes
Illustrated by Caryl Buhler
Set in various sizes of Lubalin Graph and ComicsCartoon

AND NOW A MESSAGE FROM OUR CORPORATE LAWYER:

AND NOW A MESSAGE FROM KLINK'S ELECTRONIC REPAIR SHOP:

Magnetic fields can ruin your TV picture, video and audio tapes, credit card coding, and computer disks. Keep any magnets at least a foot away from any of these things.

AND NOW A MESSAGE FROM YOUR SCHOOL NURSE:

Magnets are not for eating or swallowing. Keep them out of your mouth, nose, ears, and so forth. And keep them away from smaller kids who tend to put EVERYTHING in their mouths, noses, ears, and so forth.

MAGNETS. GET TO KNOW THEM.

Turn them one way and they stick. Turn them the other way and they scatter. What? Why? Are they WEIRD? Actually, no, they're not. Weird means unusual. Magnets are VERY common. In fact, the planet you're living on is a big magnet. And magnetic rocks come exploding out whenever a volcano blows its top.

Let's get to know **your magnets** that come with *Magnetude*. They didn't come exploding out of a volcano. But they did come out of a furnace. They're called ceramic magnets—ceramic because they're baked like pottery. They're a mix of metal powders, baked and molded while the force of a big, powerful magnet is pulling on the metal powder. When the powder cools and hardens, it's magnetic. The molded shape stays magnetic for a long time.

All magnets (Earth included) have a north pole and a south pole. Now what do they say when a muskrat and a penguin fall in love? (Pssst... major hint: "Opposites Attract.") Well, it's the same with magnets. The north pole of one magnet and the south pole of another magnet

attract. And the north pole of one magnet and the north pole of another magnet can't stand each other's guts. Same with the two south poles. They repel.

The poles on **your *Magnetude* bar magnets** are easy to see. The N shows the north-seeking pole; the S shows the south-seeking pole.

The flat magnets are a little more mysterious. Their poles are their entire flat surfaces, top and bottom. And they're not marked. Ha!

Get to know your magnets. Play with them. Try to make them levitate. Check to see whether the tip of your nose attracts or repels them.

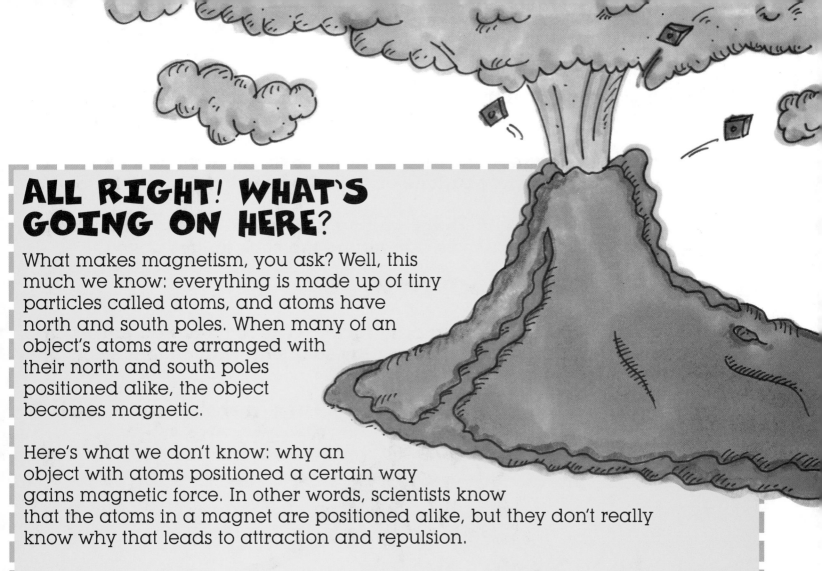

ALL RIGHT! WHAT'S GOING ON HERE?

What makes magnetism, you ask? Well, this much we know: everything is made up of tiny particles called atoms, and atoms have north and south poles. When many of an object's atoms are arranged with their north and south poles positioned alike, the object becomes magnetic.

Here's what we don't know: why an object with atoms positioned a certain way gains magnetic force. In other words, scientists know that the atoms in a magnet are positioned alike, but they don't really know why that leads to attraction and repulsion.

And if thinking about that gives you a headache, think about this: scientists know that aspirin gets rid of headaches, **but they don't really know why**.

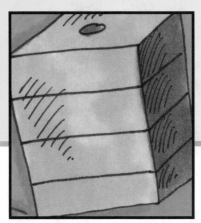

STACKING 'EM UP

Many of the stunts in this book refer to a Stack O' Magnets. Making a stack is simple. Just pile up your flat magnets and use the stack as if it were one big magnet.

SOCK BAIT

1. Fetch a sock from the hamper. Those thin, black socks that old guys wear work best. If you're too queasy to touch it, use a stick.

2. Drop a flat magnet into the toe of the sock and lay the sock like a reptile on a slippery surface—a table top or kitchen floor is good.

3. "Tease" the sock with name-calling and a Stack O' Magnets. Bring the stack as close as you can before the sock lunges at you.

Yeeeoooowww!

Nobody wants to get nailed by a dirty sock!!!! (The least-nailed person in eight hours wins.) Of course, you can play sock bait with a clean sock, or even with just the magnets and no sock.

But where's the danger? Where's the fun?

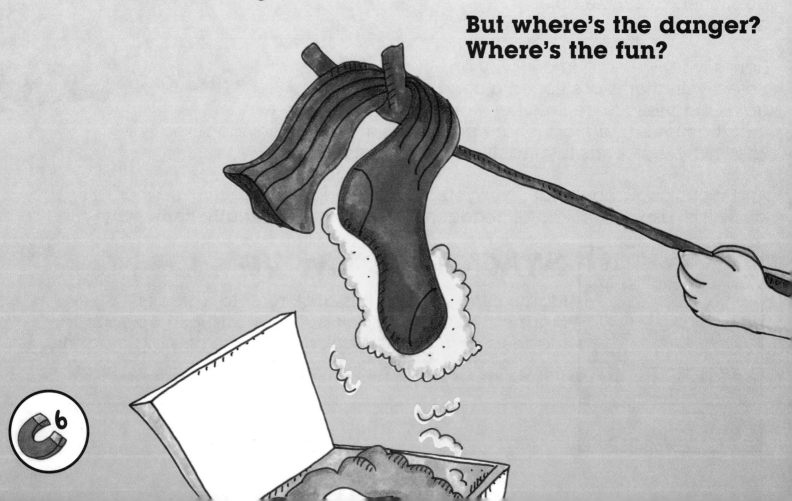

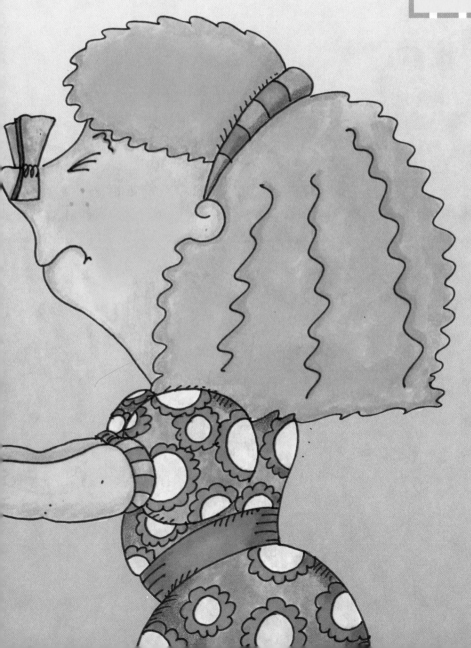

KISS & YELL

Eventually you'll go to a teen party. And you know what teens do. Dance and gossip and fall in love. Dancing and gossiping is easy. Falling in love, well... Everybody has the same question: WITH WHO? (Or as some teens say, "with whom?") Luckily there's a way to find out. It's the closest thing to kissing without kissing, and it will tell you for sure if there's an attraction.

Or not.

All you need is two people, two flat magnets, and two toothpicks. Stand face to face with the toothpicks clenched in your teeth and your lips closed tightly. Perch a magnet on the end of each toothpick (using the holes, silly!). Slowly but surely bring your faces and the ends of the toothpicks closer and closer. Just a little closer. Maybe just a litttttle clos...

POP!

What happened? Attraction? Or repulsion? Now you know. Magnetism doesn't lie. Now you can get on with the dancing and gossiping.

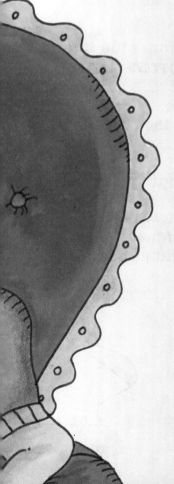

SURPRISE!

There's no practical way to predict what's going to happen. You might have the positive side facing outward and your partner might have the negative. Or the other way around. That's attraction! Or you might have both positives or negatives facing outward. Oops! Repulsion! That's the mystery of love.

WHOA!
WHAT'S GOING ON HERE?

Whether a pole is north-seeking or south-seeking is not visible to the naked eye. Or to an eye wearing a small seersucker suit, for that matter.

9

KITES. ANYWHERE. ANYTIME.

You can now fly kites at picnics regardless of the wind. You can even fly them at home in your kitchens or bedrooms, or—get this—while taking a bath.

IT'S WILD. IT'S REVOLUTIONARY.
IT'S MAGNETIC.
LET'S TAKE A LOOK.

1. Place a Stack O' Magnets wherever you want to fly a kite (hang them from a table lamp with a string, grab hold of a lamp shade or curtain by catching it between two of the magnets in the stack, or just have your buddy hold the magnets in an outstretched hand).

2. Tie a length of sewing thread to one end of a paper clip. The thinner the thread, the better. Better yet, if someone in your house has long hair, **borrow one**.

3. Get the lightest paper you can find. Old gift-wrapping paper works great. Charming, too. Cut out a kite in the shape of your choice, about the same length as the paper clip.

4. Tape the paper clip to the back of your kite, with the thread hanging downward.

5. Stick the kite to the stack of magnets and begin pulling gently down on the other end of the thread. Sooner or later the kite will break free of the magnets, but stay floating in the magnetic field. Ha! You have triumphed. You are no longer tied to the whim of the cruel April wind.

YOU MAY FLY A KITE ANYWHERE.
ANYTIME.
FOR ANY REASON.

KNOW WHAT WOULD BE REALLY COOL?

Stick a row of flat magnets under a window sill. Maybe you can use thumb tacks or tape. (If you don't want a lecture, make sure nobody can see the tack holes.) Make a bunch of kites in different colors and shapes and sizes and have them all flying at the same time. It would be like having a permanent flying kite collection.

WHICH ONES DO YOU THINK WOULD FLY FURTHER FROM THE MAGNET?

THE BIG ONES?

THE SMALL ONES?

THE RED ONES?

THE ONES THAT USE A HAIR FOR A STRING INSTEAD OF A THREAD?

HELLO! WHAT'S GOING ON HERE?

Magnetic force keeps on pulling and pulling, even when it can't quite win the tug of war.

13

FESTIVE WINTER BRAIN FREEZE

Here's a great way to decorate your desk or table top for the winter. That is...heh, heh...if you have **NERVES OF STEEL!!!!**

The idea is to arrange your six bar magnets into a beautiful snowflake design on a smooth desk or table top. The challenge is to set up the magnets so they don't scoot around and mess up the design.

What's the matter? The south poles don't want to snuggle up to the south poles? Well then, what if you put a south pole next to a north pole, next to a south pole, next to a...

Okay, try again. Maybe you're being too rough. Be a little gentler. Okay, maybe a little s l o w e r. Try holding your breath this time. Maybe if you just ease the magnets into position using a stick or a pencil point. How about if you click your heels together three times? Try changing your shirt.

WHAT **IS** THE DEAL?
IT LOOKS SO EASY!

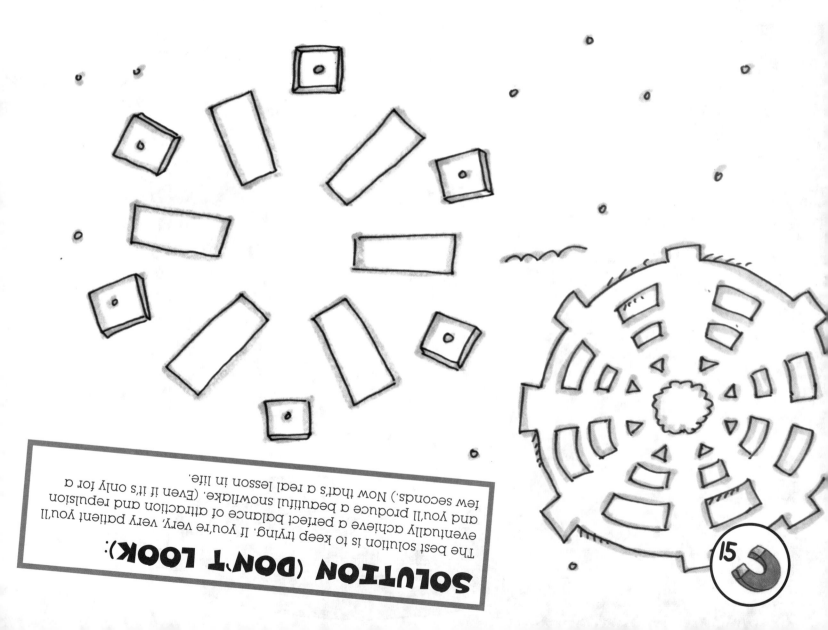

HMMMM! WHAT'S GOING ON HERE?

Since you can't see magnetic fields, trying to balance the fields of six magnets is darn near impossible. But it CAN be done! Keep Trying!

SOLUTION (DON'T LOOK):

The best solution is to keep trying. If you're very, very patient you'll eventually achieve a perfect balance of attraction and repulsion and you'll produce a beautiful snowflake. (Even if it's only for a few seconds.) Now that's a real lesson in life.

15

HENWAY, THE NEXT GENERATION

This is a humdinger of a joke that dates back to the days of Genghis Khan (about the year 1200). This magnetic version was introduced on Planet Dexter much more recently—about 400 Dexter years ago.

STEP 1: Hold a flat magnet under the front of your shirt. Shirts of thin material work best.

STEP 2: Place a second magnet on the outside of your shirt, over the first magnet. They'll stick together **THROUGH YOUR SHIRT MATERIAL.** Cool. And this isn't even the good part.

STEP 3: Walk around with the magnet stuck to your shirt and identify a victim. Adults who are busy eating or reading always make good victims.

STEP 4: Walk up and address your victim. "Hi there" is a good line. The victim will likely turn your way, squint, and respond, "What's that on your shirt?"

STEP 5: You answer very casually, "It's a henway." In 83% of cases, the victim will respond with the question "What's a henway?"

STEP 6: Pause one second, then reply "Oh, about three or four pounds!!!" Now cluck and cackle in a burst of laughter.

You've done it!

EGAD! WHAT'S GOING ON HERE?

A little cloth can't stop the power of magnetism!

ASK UNCLE CHESTER

THE AGE-OLD SAGE OF PLANET DEXTER. HE'S DONE IT ALL. HE'S SEEN IT ALL. HE KNOWS IT ALL. JUST ASK HIM.

DEAR UNCLE CHESTER,

I'm in trouble again. My principal was giving us a speech about good manners yesterday. He started coughing, so my teacher asked me to get him a glass of water. But while I was carrying it up to the front of the room, Jackie Judson flipped a bottle cap into the glass and it sank to the bottom. I didn't know what to do. All the kids were laughing, the principal was coughing, and I was standing there. So I stuck my fingers in the glass and tried to fish the bottle cap out. Big mistake. My teacher grabbed me and told me I had bad manners for sticking my fingers in the principal's glass. Before I could explain, she told me I had to write a 10-page report about good manners. I'm extremely peeved. Did anything like this ever happen to you?

                                    —JIMMY

DEAR JIMMY,

Of course. I was traveling to Paris on the Concorde with Walt Disney's grandfather one night when I accidentally dropped my Super Bowl Ring into his grapefruit juice. Could have been a disaster, but my oversized brain saved the day. Pour yourself a glass of water, drop in a paper clip, sit back, relax, and let me explain. Now think about it. How are you going to get that clip out? Fingers? Certainly not. That <u>is</u> bad manners, you oaf. Would you use a spoon? Nope, too obvious. Dump the water out? Too messy. The answer is to hold a flat or bar magnet against the outside of the glass near the paper clip. The magnetic field will GO THROUGH THE GLASS AND THROUGH THE WATER and attract the clip. Now just move the magnet nonchalantly up the side of the glass and boink! Out comes the clip, like magic. If you want to stay out of--heh,heh--hot water with teachers and major celebrities, you'll always carry a Lucky Magnet with you. Just like your Uncle Chester does.

-UNCLE CHESTER

PSSST! WHAT'S GOING ON HERE?

Magnetic force not only goes through glass and water, but it goes through glass and water at the same time, keeping you out of all kinds of trouble.

19

QUEASY THREESIES & THE YUCK MAGNET

It's important to build courage in your younger pals. Fortitude. Grit. Mettle. That kind of stuff.

Tell your young friends to imagine the grossest item they can think of. Unrefrigerated squid brains. Week-old Fish 'N Liver leftovers. A pie full of banana spiders. A greasy stuffed cabbage hiding under the refrigerator. EEeeYewww! Phenomenally pungent!

Now place a flat magnet on a smooth table or kitchen floor. Tell your friends all the greasy griminess they've just imagined has been transferred to the magnet. The magnet IS the squid brains or the pie (or worse). We'll call it the **YUCK magnet.** And you want them to put a **YUCK magnet** IN THEIR POCKETS!

First show them how to use another flat magnet to move the **YUCK magnet** around the floor without touching it. (You know, by repelling it). If that's not enough, show your little friend how to use yet another flat magnet to repel the middle flat magnet. And have the middle flat magnet repelling the YUCK magnet. This three-magnet combination is called **QUEASY THREESIES** and it looks very cool to do. Soon your young friends will be begging you to let them try. That's a sign their courage is growing.

Have a **QUEASY THREESIES** race. See who can get the **YUCK magnet** across the table or floor the fastest. Now you're cooking. Soon they'll feel right at home with the **YUCK magnet**. They'll be able to touch it and pick it up and play with it. When the time is right, suggest they put it in their pockets. Tell them how courageous they are. Then remind them. They have squid brains in their pockets.

WOW! WHAT'S GOING ON HERE?

Using magnetic repulsion to move magnets across a floor without touching them is a neat game of science and skill and a great lesson in imaginary courage.

21

THE HAUNTED BATHROOM

It's not Planet Dexter's job to tell you, but there are times when you shouldn't bother people in the bathroom. Then again, there are other times when it is **MANDATORY** to bother people in the bathroom. Like when cousins or friends are visiting, for instance. When they scream and run after you, just remember to plead the cause of Science.

The first thing you need is an item that is light in weight and dark in color. Something that can swing freely from the bathroom door's inside doorknob or robe hook. A dark silk tie or scarf is perfect. A belt can work, too. (This works only if the bathroom door is made of wood, not steel.)

1. Place one end of the item between two **FLAT** magnets, letting the magnets latch together through the material. You'll want a dark item so the magnets won't be too conspicuous.

2. Loop the item over the doorknob or hook. Make a mental note of the magnets' position on the inside of the door—and the matching area on the outside of the door.

3. Offer your visitor ample beverages and wait patiently. Iced tea and diet colas seem to be especially effective.

4. As soon as your visitor enters the bathroom, spring into action with a Stack O' Magnets. Move the stack in and out and back and forth at the proper position on your side of the door. Attract and repel the magnets on the belt or tie **RIGHT THROUGH THE DOOR!** The tie or belt will dance and swing, and you'll hear it brushing against the door. With a little practice beforehand, you can make the item do the twist, the hully gully, the watusi, all those wacky dances! To the bathroom occupant, the effect is uncanny... and extremely creepy.

5. When you hear a scream, stand back. The occupant will soon crash through the door, creating a big hole that exactly matches his or her shape, just like in the cartoons.

OOOOOOH! WHAT'S GOING ON HERE?

Magnetic force sneaking through wood
can produce a shriek that's especially good.

24

MAGNETISM: NOT EVERYONE'S CUP OF TEA

It's true. Earth is a big magnet, and nearly every modern appliance and entertainment device depends on magnets. But that doesn't mean you have to like them. In fact, many people find them too grabby. Others feel repulsed by them one day; attracted the next.

Well, now, you can do something about unwanted magnetism. Using the Dextronic Magneutralizer Technique, you can free your paper clips and other valuables from the grasp of the magnetic menace.

LET'S LOOK AT A LITTLE SCENARIO, SHALL WE?

Imagine a FLAT magnet is holding your favorite large paper clip hostage (little paper clips don't work as well). Dastardly. But you're not helpless. Simply approach the offending magnet from above with a Stack O' Magnets, repulsion side down. The offending magnet, coward that it is, will drop your clip like a hot potato. That's the Dextronic Magneutralizer Technique.

Cool, eh?

YO! WHAT'S GOING ON HERE?

By itself, the single magnet attracts your clip. By itself, the Stack O' Magnets attracts your clip. But bring the stack and the single magnet together in repelling mode and the magnetic fields cancel each other out. Your clip is free! Just in time to go back into its little box for the night.

BALLET ON THE CEILING

Ever wonder about ballet? Everyone's spinning around on their toes. **Why not just hire taller people?**

On Planet Dexter, of course, ballet is performed in unusual places, like on ceilings. Really. And you can try it here on Earth with an empty glass, a Stack O' Magnets, and a paper clip.

Hold the magnets on the outside bottom of the glass and drop the paper clip in the glass. Now turn the glass over with the magnets still in place and the clip sticking to the bottom (which is now on top). Slowly lift the Stack O' Magnets upward from the glass, maintaining the magnets' invisible attraction to the clip. When the clip appears to hang loosely from the er, uh, "ceiling," the show is about to begin. Move the magnets in circles above the glass and the clip will spin and pirouette and do all kinds of ballet moves. With a little practice you'll have the clip spinning so fast, it will be just a blur. A graceful blur.

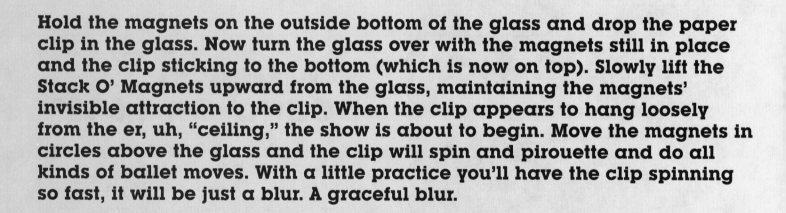

SHOW TIME

Put *Swan Lake* on the stereo. Turn out the room lamps and shine a flashlight through the glass for a spotlight. Speak nothing but French.

Celebrate the performance afterward with French fries.

28

I SAY! WHAT'S GOING ON HERE?

Even at a distance, through a glass, and jiggling all over the place, magnetic force is strong enough to entertain.

CELEBRITY MAGNET TOSS

Here's a game of skill for two or more people that combines the glamour of Hollywood and the magnetic attractiveness of most refrigerators. It's also a swell way to win mouth-watering treats and refreshments. And for the losers... well, **you'll see.**

First, go through your newspaper recycling pile and cut out pictures of eleven of your favorite stars (use fewer pictures for a shorter game). Stick the pictures to the refrigerator, using your flat and bar magnets, putting aside one flat magnet for tossing purposes.

Now, standing about five feet away from the refrigerator, take turns tossing your remaining flat magnet at the celebrities, one by one. Starting with the picture in the upper left-hand corner, you have to bean each celebrity in succession, from left to right, working your way down the fridge. You can't move on to the next until you bean the one before. Take turns, one toss at a time, and work your way through to the last celebrity.

THERE'S MORE →

31

Whoever gets there first—ya hootie dootie!—wins. The winner gloats and opens the fridge to enjoy the snack of his or her choice, AND... to pick snacks for the LOSERS! Imagine the possibilities! Those green olives with the red things (pimentos) in them! Hot dog relish without the hot dog! Leftover lima beans!

Remember, this is supposed to create fun, not bellyaches or medical emergencies. No medicine, alcohol, or raw meat or fish! And nothing spoiled!

Be smart and funny, not mean!

HEY KIDS!

Try For Free Visits With Your Favorite Celebrities!

It's easy. Just write your favorite celebrity a letter. Ask him or her if you can have a free visit. You can mention Planet Dexter's Celebrity Magnet Toss if you think it would help!

OUCH! WHAT'S GOING ON HERE?

Nothing. Just having some fun.

DO YOU MIND?

INTRUDER DETECTOR

This is a great way to find out if anyone's been snooping around in your stuff. Just lay a bar magnet on your books, for instance. Lean the other bar magnet over it, like so:

Patience, patience.
You'll get it. Uh, eventually.

The north pole of the bottom magnet will repel the north pole of the top magnet, causing the north end of the top magnet to hover in the air.

The slightest movement will knock the magnets out of the hovering mode and you'll know that someone's been rooting through your stuff. Or that a gust of wind came by. Or that the 5:15 train just pulled in at the station.

REMEMBER:

It's a good thing this takes some time to set up. If it was quick and easy, the intruder could root through your stuff and then just set the magnets up again. But don't worry. Intruders rarely have the patience for science.

SSSSSH! WHAT'S GOING ON HERE?

The force of magnetic repulsion is stronger than the weight of the top magnet.

MAGNAWEEGEE
YOUR MAGNETIC ADVISOR.

EVERY WONDER WHAT THE HECK TO DO NEXT?
ASK THE MAGNAWEEGEE.

One swing of the MagnaWeeGee pendulum and you'll gain valuable recommendations about what to do next. If you're not satisfied with the answer, just try again. MagnaWeeGee won't mind.

SETTING UP THE MAGNAWEEGEE

1. Make a magical mystical magnetic pendulum pointer from a paper clip and sewing thread.

2. Hang the pendulum from a lamp or tape it under a kitchen table—anywhere it can swing freely with the paper clip about an INCH above your opened book.

3. Flip ahead to page 37. Place one flat magnet in each of the six pink blocks arranged in a circle.

35

4. Move the book (carefully, so you don't scramble your setup) until the mystical magical magnetic pendulum is hanging directly over the **"All Knowing, All Powerful"** emblem in the center of the circle. Be patient. The MagnaWeeGee is about to tell you

WHAT TO DO NEXT . . .

TO CONSULT THE MAGNAWEEGEE

Just give the mystical magical magnetic pendulum a shove and chant over and over again, in a low mysterious voice, "The MagnaWeeGee Knows All, The MagnaWeeGee Knows All." Eventually, the mystical magnetic forces entrusted to the Royal Order of MagnaWeeGee will capture your pendulum pointer.

AND YOU'LL FIND OUT WHAT TO DO NEXT!!!

Note: There are two reasons the MagnaWeeGee may produce unsatisfactory results. They are both your fault. Nothing is the MagnaWeeGee's fault.

1. You started with the pendulum hanging too close or too far from the "All Knowing, All Powerful" emblem. Adjust the distance.

2. You're not chanting with your voice low enough or mysterious enough.

KEEP TRYING.

KADABRA! WHAT'S GOING ON HERE?

Magicians and other tricksters have been capturing items in magnetic fields for years and telling people it's magic. Don't be fooled by cheap imitations. The MagnaWeeGee is real.*

* Printed on 100% real paper, that is.

36

Flush the Toilet

Eat Something

Go Ahead and Call Him or Her

Inspect Your Socks for Holes

ALL KNOWING

CIRCLE
OF
RECOMMENDATIONS

ALL POWERFUL

See What's in the Refrigerator

Count All the Windows in Your House and Divide by Three

Answer the Phone Whether It Rings or Not

Wash Behind Your Ears

37

SLICK ULTRACOOLNESS

Before you go to bed tonight, you should:
1. brush your teeth, and
2. put six bar magnets face down (with the N and S poles toward the bottom of the tray) in water in an ice-cube tray in your freezer (muffin pans or egg cartons work fine, too).

WHEN YOU WAKE UP, YOU'LL HAVE:

1. fresh breath, and
2. some real cool magnetic fun.

When the cubes freeze solid, empty the tray onto a dinner plate. Flip all the N and S sides upward and watch the fun begin.

Try to stop all the MagnaCubes from eventually lining up north to south to north to south to north to south to so on and so on.

GO AHEAD. TRY.

38

THERE'S MORE →

39

It's no illusion that magnets are stronger when cold.

WHY?

Cold temperatures slow the movement of atoms. In a cold magnet, the atoms stay in their north/south positions even more stubbornly than usual. And this north/south positioning of atoms is what creates magnetism in the first place. (See "Magnets: Get To Know Them" for more about that).

BRRR! WHAT'S GOING ON HERE?

A lot! Friction occurs when two or more items rub against each other. It slows things down. The ice reduces friction, so the magnetic action speeds up. At the same time, the ice cools the magnets down and makes them stronger. So everything gets faster and stronger. Cool!

ICE MELTED?

The fun's not over yet. All six cold magnets will be very eager to jump into a chain that you can pick up and carry around. The chain won't be so strong in half an hour when the magnets (and the atoms they're made of) are warmed up to room temperature. As the famous Viking Erik the Red once said: "I always feel stronger on a cold day." Same with magnets.

STROLLING WITH YOUR MAGNETS ON A SUNDAY AFTERNOON

Here's a way to get iron particles, fresh air, and exercise by taking your flat magnets for a walk. On a leash.

After all, Earth is 35% iron, isn't it? That would be a chunk about one-third the size of the Earth. So it stands to reason that there's some iron on the sidewalk in front of your house, and in your driveway, and on the beach.

First, jam a plastic sandwich bag into your pocket (a Ziplock is perfect). Then grab a Stack O' Magnets and tie a leash-length string through the magnets' holes. Tie a knot that's big enough to keep the magnets from sliding off as you drag them around the neighborhood.

Now start walking. Drag the magnets anywhere you see specks of sand or dirt (try the sides of roads and rusty areas—like those areas around rain drain pipes). Ignore the stares of your neighbors. They walk silly, scrawny dogs with bulging eyes. You're on a mission of science. Check your magnets once in a while and you'll find a growing beard of iron particles. Every once in a while scrape them off the magnets and into your plastic sandwich bag.

When you have enough (a teaspoonful is plenty), wash your hands (you've basically been attracting dirt). Put your bag of iron particles away for later, and pour yourself a lemonade. There's nothing better than enjoying a lemonade after walking your magnets.

42

TIP #47: MAKING UNCLE CHESTER FLIP HIS WIG

Remember that know-it-all Uncle Chester? Let's get him. Sprinkle some of your iron particles on his dome (head) to make an attractive toupee. When you're ready to see him flip his wig, just put a magnet under the page. Bzzzz. Instant Mohawk.

GADZOOKS! WHAT'S GOING ON HERE?

Iron is everywhere. You just have to know how to "attract" it.

ANNOYING PIRATES

Whether you ever have been—or expect to be—kidnapped by pirates, it will pay to learn this little maneuver. With it, you can turn a ship's compass into a whirling merry-go-round, drive the captain and crew batty, and escape in a lifeboat during all the confusion.

44

To practice for this adventure, you'll need:
1. a soup bowl nearly full of water
2. a smaller dish or saucer to float on the water
3. tape (such as Scotch tape)
4. something that looks like a telescope
    (an empty paper-towel roll is perfect)
5. your bar magnets

Float the smaller dish in the soup bowl and place a BAR magnet in the center of the smaller dish. The magnet and dish will eventually swing around and line up with Earth's north/south magnetic field. Any magnet allowed to move freely will do this.

Now, in case you haven't noticed, they usually keep the telescope near the compass on a pirate ship. It's a way to pass the time when the captain isn't swashbuckling. Check the compass, look through the telescope. Check the compass, look through the telescope. And that's your opportunity! What would happen if you hid magnets in that telescope? Let's find out.

Tape a few bar magnets end to end inside your paper-towel roll and lay the "telescope" next to your compass (an inch or two away is fine). There! Now what direction is north? The compass lines up with your "telescope." You've overruled Earth's magnetic field!

If you were actually at sea, and if it were an actual compass and an actual telescope, the rest would be simple. After putting the magnets in the telescope, you would just go to the bow of the ship and yell "Ship Ahoy!" The captain would grab the telescope for a look, see nothing, and slam it down next to the compass, cussing and muttering. Then you would sneak to the stern of the ship and yell "Ship Ahoy!" and he'd do the same thing. Meanwhile the compass would be going crazy, and so would the crew! Everybody would be yelling and fighting, and you could slip quietly into the dinghy and cast off to freedom!

AHOY! WHAT'S GOING ON HERE?

Normally, Earth's north magnetic pole pulls on the north-seeking pole of any free-swinging magnet. It's not a very strong pull—the pull of any nearby magnet is probably stronger.

47

SEEING THE INVISIBLE, MAN

And you thought magnetic fields were invisible. Well, here's a way to get an eyeful. Call your local steamship company and book passage to Narvik, Norway, or anywhere above the Arctic Circle. That's close to where Earth's magnetic field meets the magnetic north pole. And if you happen to be in Narvik on a clear night, and the sun has recently shot off a solar flare (very common), you'll see the result of particles from the flare (called the solar wind) getting caught in Earth's magnetic field. It's the Aurora Borealis (uh-ROAR-uh bore-ee-AL-iss). It's gorgeous, like a ghostly green curtain billowing thousands of miles across the night sky.

What? You lost your steamer schedule? All right then, we'll create our own version, which we call the "Aurora Dirty Alice."

Put a bar magnet on the page under the Aurora Dirty Alice Viewing Screen and sprinkle some of the iron dirt (that stuff you collected in "strolling with your magnets") on top of the Screen. Sprinkle it right on top of where the magnet is. Then tap the viewing screen lightly with your finger until the iron dirt jumps around and forms visible lines around the magnet. The iron dirt particles get caught in the magnet's magnetic field the same way that the solar wind particles get caught in Earth's magnetic field.

There you have it, the Aurora Dirty Alice. Not as romantic as the real thing, but think of the savings in steamer fare.

ZOUNDS! WHAT'S GOING ON HERE?

Imagine pure magnetic power, all squeezed together, coming out of your bar magnet at its north pole. Once in the air, the power spreads out, curves around, and travels through the air to the magnet's south pole. Here it bunches together again and enters the magnet's south pole. The power then travels upward through the magnet to the north pole again. It reenters the air for another trip to the south pole and then through the magnet to the north pole. The cycle goes on and on. That's basically the nature of magnetic fields. Naturally, wherever the force is bunched together you'll have the strongest magnetism. And that's why—whether you're looking at the Aurora Borealis or Dirty Alice—you'll see most of the particles at the poles.

ORANGE YOU GLAD WE LIVE ON THE CRUST?

The biggest magnet on Earth is, uh, the Earth. Let's see.... It weighs 6,595,000,000,000,000,000,000 tons. It's 25,000 miles around at the equator. And you would have to tunnel 8,000 miles to get to the other side. Yep. That's a big magnet, all right. And a good way to understand a theory about Earth's magnetism is to squash an orange.

Oh, go ahead. You know you want to do it. Grab a big juicy orange and drop, squeeze, and roll it until it gets nice and mushy inside (don't break the skin). Once you can hear liquid moving around inside (and is the skin still intact), the orange has become just like Earth.

Yes indeed. Look at the orange and imagine this: we live on Earth's outer skin, called Earth's crust, which is about 20 miles thick. Below that there is the mantle, a layer of solid rock. Then, at the center of the Earth, there's the core—rocks so hot they've melted. It's liquid inside Earth, just as it is inside the orange (only about 1,400 degrees hotter).

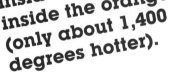

And just like it does in the orange, the liquid sloshes around in there. Earth is spinning and wobbling, and the hot, molten rock is spinning and churning, faster in some areas, slower in others. This circular movement of Earth's liquid core is one of the explanations for Earth's magnetic field.

As the magnetic force is generated, it magnetizes metallic rocks inside Earth. Sometimes these rocks come exploding out of the Earth in volcanic eruptions.

It is thought that the first known magnets were some of these volcanic rocks found in a region of western Asia called Magnesia. Get the connection? Magnets? Magnesia? Makes sense, no?

Now, you want to see a volcano? Poke a hole in the orange and squeeeeeeeze.

AAAAIEEEE! RUN FOR YOUR LIVES! THAT JUICE IS FLOWING AT 1,400 DEGREES AND IT'S HEADING RIGHT FOR THE VILLAGE! RUN! RUN FOR THE SEA!

JUST KIDDING.

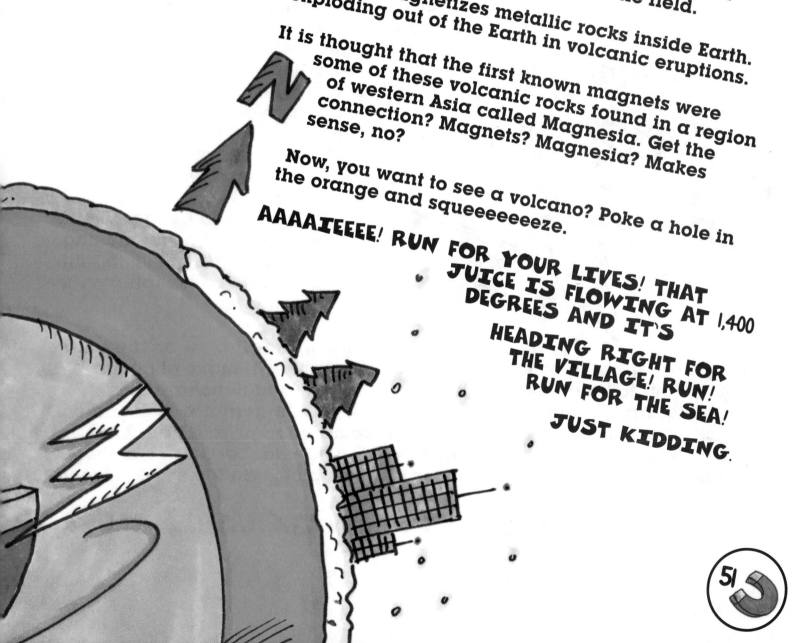

51

HEY KIDS! EARN EXTRA CASH IN YOUR SPARE TIME!

Did you ever shuffle across a room, looking for something to do, when ZAP! you touch a doorknob or TV set and get a little shock? That's called static electricity, and here's how to use static electricity to make some real money!

On a day when you're getting those little zaps (usually a cool, clear, dry day), tell a companion to lend you a nickel and you'll perform a spectacular trick for his or her entertainment. Patiently stand the nickel on its edge and lower a toothpick across it until the toothpick balances. Now place a drinking glass over the nickel and toothpick. Tell your companion to try to move the toothpick without touching the glass or moving the table or stomping on the floor.

Now the fun begins. They'll blow on the glass. Clap near it. Yell next to it. Oh, what buffoons they'll make of themselves. You'll want to laugh, but don't. Just act as cool and nonchalant as possible. Tap your toe, whistle idly, check your fingernails, look at the clock, and—above all—casually run a comb through your hair. After a while they'll give up, exasperated. Now's your chance. Glance at them impatiently and ask "If I can move the toothpick, can I keep the nickel?"

"ANYTHING, ANYTHING," IS THE USUAL REPLY.

With that, simply hold your comb close to the glass. The toothpick will twitch, and you'll be five cents richer. Perform the routine 20 times and you'll have a dollar. Perform it 300,000 times and you'll have enough to buy a Mazda Miata. **Now that's real money.**

HI HO! WHAT'S GOING ON HERE?

What you're really using is static electricity, a relative of magnetism. When you comb your hair you rub some electrons (particles of atoms) off the comb and into your hair. The comb wants to replace its lost electrons so it begins pulling them from any objects nearby—including the pivoting toothpick, which swings around trying to hold onto its electrons.

53

OH, DRY UP...

Static electricity stunts work best when the air is dry BECAUSE less water vapor in the air means more rubbing between the comb and your hair. HUH? Yeah, water tends to lubricate. Same thing when you're walking across a rug. The drier the day, the bigger the shocks. (If you try this rug thing in the dark, you can actually see the sparks.)

55

GIVE YOURSELF A MAGNETIC PERSONALITY

You've seen the type. A guest walks into a party. Beverages and cheese balls fall to the floor as everyone flocks to the door with greetings, compliments, and offers of refreshments. "Hello, gorgeous. I love your hat. Can I get you a cheese ball?" Guests like this are said to have magnetic personalities. For some reason, they're very personally attractive. And for the average schmoe trying to play pranks and have fun, they're a royal pain. They steal the audience.

THERE'S MORE →

THE NEXT TIME YOU'RE AT A PARTY, FIGHT BACK. PROVE TO EVERYONE THAT YOU HAVE A MAGNETIC PERSONALITY AND DESERVE PLENTY OF ATTENTION, TOO.

1. First thing to do is bug your host for scissors, a sheet of paper (typing paper is best), Scotch-type tape, and a paper clip.

2. Straighten out the paper clip, rebend it into the shape shown and tape it to the table so one end is sticking straight up.

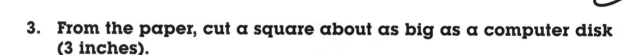

3. From the paper, cut a square about as big as a computer disk (3 inches).

4. Fold the square diagonally, then open it and fold it diagonally again. When you open the paper now it should look like a pyramid that's been stepped on by a giant mallard.

5. Set the paper "pyramid" on the tip of the paper clip. It should revolve easily and evenly and eventually stop.

6. Gain the attention of the crowd. Duck calls are always effective. Announce that by the power of your magnetic personality, you will now cause the paper square to rotate without touching it or blowing on it. Demand complete silence from the crowd.

7. Cup your hands under the paper square. Scrunch your eyebrows as if you are concentrating in a some sort of magnetic fashion. The paper will eventually begin to rotate one way, then the other. If the paper is especially well-balanced it may rotate continually.

THERE YOU HAVE IT. PROOF POSITIVE THAT YOU, TOO, HAVE A MAGNETIC PERSONALITY. DON'T BE SURPRISED IF A LINE FORMS SO GUESTS CAN TAKE TURNS DANCING WITH YOU.

CAN YOU SPELL H-O-A-X?

Go ahead. Enjoy the party. At the end you can find out who your real friends are by announcing that the whole thing is a sham. People don't have magnetic powers. They don't have magnetic fields. The mysterious force that moved the paper is simply body heat rising from your hands. Really.

LEVITATION. THE NEXT BIG FAD.

Did you ever want to just levitate something? You know, make it float in the air? Well then, this is your big break.

Don't laugh. Scientists on Earth are working on something called MAGLEV (get it? MAG for magnetic, LEV for levitation?) that uses magnets to levitate train cars ABOVE the tracks as they run. No clicketies, no clacketies—just very high speed.

BUT WHY WAIT TO LEVITATE?

Just put two flat magnets together with the **LEVITATING CORNER** between them. In the same way, put two more flat magnets on the same corner of pages 63 and 64. Make sure the two sets of magnets are repelling each other. And hold on to your hat, because you're heading into the future. **The LEVITATING CORNER IS LEVITATING!!!!**

ANOTHER MARVEL: PREDICTING THE FUTURE

Do you know what's going to happen? After the initial astonishment wears off and you pick your jaw up off the floor, you'll start to play. You'll poke the top magnet to make it bounce and you'll stick paper clips and bar magnets into the levitation field to see what happens. You think you won't. But you will. We know. On Planet Dexter we can predict the future fairly accurately. We wouldn't even be surprised if you went to sleep with the page levitating next to your bed—just to see if it levitates all night (the page, not your bed!).

ZOWIE! WHAT'S GOING ON HERE?

Each set of magnets is locked onto its page by attraction, yet each set is repelling the other set with a force strong enough to lift and keep a book page in the air.

ATOMIC CRAZINESS

Imagine people at an amusement park. What would happen if you got on the Ferris wheel, went to the top, pulled out a bullhorn and began to sing the theme from *The Addams Family*? If you were loud enough, most everybody in the park would stop and turn and face in your direction.

WHY? WHO KNOWS? BUT THEY WOULD.

It's the same with magnetism. We can make the atoms in iron or steel turn and face in one direction and we don't know why! What's the attraction? It might be the same reason people turn to look at a fool singing at the top of a Ferris wheel. We don't really know. Yet.

But we do know how to keep the atoms in certain metals all facing in the same direction. Let's do it!

Just get something long and made of iron or steel, like a nail or screwdriver or letter opener. Make sure it's iron or steel by testing whether a magnet will stick to it. Now take a Stack O' Magnets and begin to stroke the metal item in one direction only, lifting the magnets off the item when you get to the end of each stroke. Do it about thirty times or more. Then try to use the iron or steel item as a magnet. Try to pick up a paper clip.

There! You've done it. You've created magnetism. You've made the atoms in the metal turn and face in one direction. And you didn't even need a bullhorn!

HOT DOG! WHAT'S GOING ON HERE?

By stroking the iron or steel item with a magnet, you transfer magnetism to it. And the magnetism is long lasting. The atoms should stay lined up unless you knock them out of kilter. Sometimes striking the item really hard with a hammer will knock the atoms out of line. And heating the item can destroy magnetism by making the atoms move around.

63